Theory Paper   Grade 2   2017   A

Duration 1½ hours

Candidates should answer ALL questions.
Write your answers on this paper – no others will be accepted.
Answers must be written clearly and neatly – otherwise marks may be lost.

100

1   Add the time signature to each of these five examples.

10

2   Write the time values ♩ ♪ ♩. ♪ ♩. ♪. in the correct order, from the **longest** to
the **shortest**. The first answer is given.

10

3

3 Rewrite this melody in the bass clef, keeping the pitch the same. The first note is given.

10

S. Heller

4 Add the correct clef and any necessary accidentals to make each of the scales named below. Do **not** use key signatures.

10

E minor

Which form of the minor scale have you used? ....

B♭ major

5 Answer **both** (a) and (b).

10

(a) Name the degree of the scale (e.g. 2nd, 3rd) of each of the notes marked *, as shown in the first answer. The key is A major.

Haydn

3rd
....

(b) Give the letter name of the first note of the melody, including the sharp sign if necessary. ....

6 **After** each note write a **higher** note to form the named **melodic** interval within the key of D major. The first answer is given. `[10]`

7th

3rd

5th

2nd

6th

8th/8ve

7 Rewrite the following melody, grouping (beaming) the notes correctly. `[10]`

8 Tick one box for each term/sign, as shown in the first answer. `[10]`

Con moto means:

more movement	☐
less movement	☐
without movement	☐
with movement	☑

Adagio means:

quick	☐
slow	☐
at a medium speed	☐
fairly quick	☐

non troppo means:

too much	☐
not in time	☐
very much	☐
not too much	☐

sostenuto means:

in the same way	☐
in the style of	☐
sustained	☐
expressive	☐

mf means:

very loud	☐
moderately quiet	☐
moderately loud	☐
loud	☐

⟋ means:

gradually getting louder	☐
gradually getting quieter	☐
gradually getting quicker	☐
gradually getting slower	☐

5

9 Look at this melody by Volkmann and then answer the questions below.

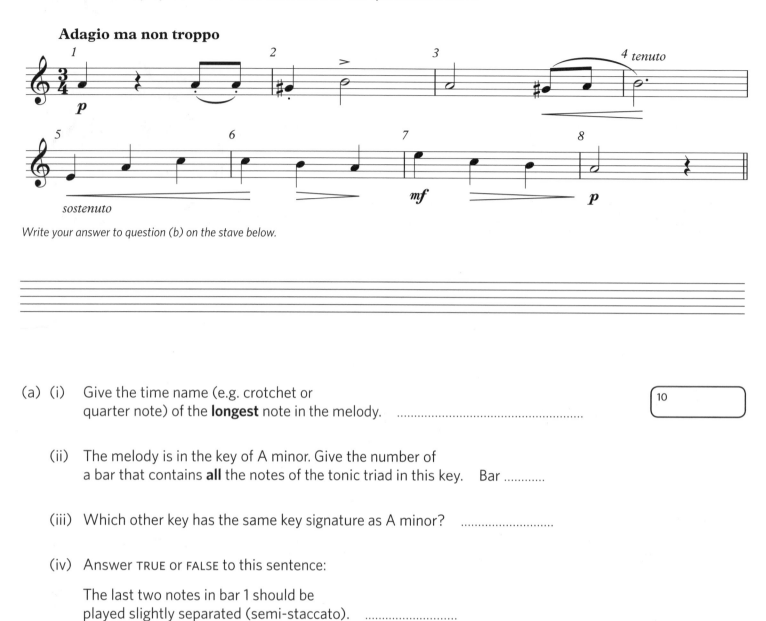

Write your answer to question (b) on the stave below.

(a) (i) Give the time name (e.g. crotchet or quarter note) of the **longest** note in the melody. ....

(ii) The melody is in the key of A minor. Give the number of a bar that contains **all** the notes of the tonic triad in this key. Bar ....

(iii) Which other key has the same key signature as A minor? ....

(iv) Answer TRUE or FALSE to this sentence:

The last two notes in bar 1 should be played slightly separated (semi-staccato). ....

(v) How many bars contain a crotchet (quarter-note) rest? ....

(b) Copy out the music from the start of bar 1 to the end of bar 4, exactly as it is written above. Don't forget the clef, time signature, tempo marking, dynamics and all other details. Write the music on the blank stave above question (a).

10

10

Theory Paper   Grade 2   2017   B

Duration 1½ hours

TOTAL MARKS
100

Candidates should answer ALL questions.
Write your answers on this paper – no others will be accepted.
Answers must be written clearly and neatly – otherwise marks may be lost.

1   Add the missing bar-lines to these two melodies. The first bar-line is given in each.

C. Loewe

2   Rewrite the following melody in notes of **half the value**, beginning as shown. Remember to group (beam) the notes correctly where necessary.

3   Rewrite this melody using the key signature of D major. Leave out all unnecessary accidentals, but remember to put in any that are needed. The first bar is given.

4 Answer **both** (a) and (b).

(a) Rewrite these treble-clef notes in the bass clef, keeping the pitch the same. The first answer is given.

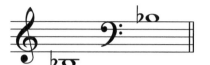  

(b) In which major key are **all** these notes found? ....

5 Name the keys of these tonic triads.

....

 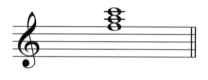

....

6 Using semibreves (whole notes), write one octave of the scales named below.

E♭ major, ascending, **with** key signature.

A minor, descending, **without** key signature but adding any necessary accidentals.

Which form of the minor scale have you used? ....

7 Add the correct clef to make each of these named notes, as shown in the first answer.

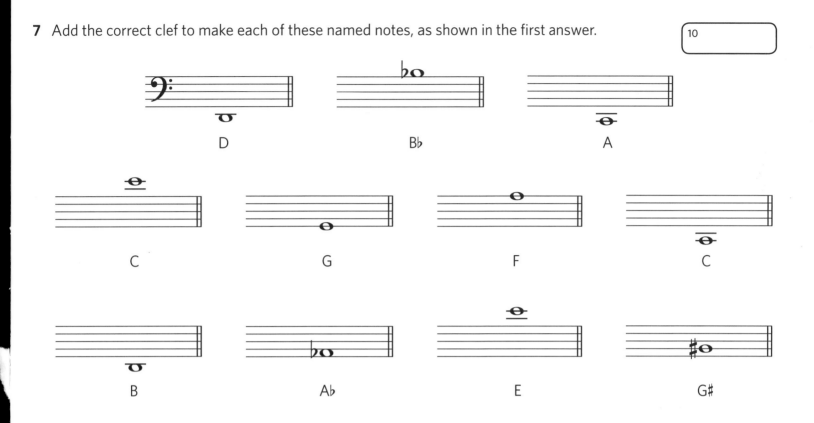

D	Bb	A
C	G	F	C
B	Ab	E	G#

8 Tick one box for each term/sign, as shown in the first answer.

simile means:

in the same way ✔

in the style of ☐

too much ☐

without ☐

Larghetto means:

rather slow ☐

smoothly ☐

very slow, solemn ☐

gradually getting slower ☐

Vivo means:

fairly quick ☐

lively, quick ☐

gradually getting quicker ☐

at a medium speed ☐

sf means:

loud, then immediately soft ☐

slight pressure ☐

staccatissimo ☐

forced, accented ☐

da capo (D. C.) means:

the end ☐

repeat from the beginning ☐

in time ☐

repeat from the sign 𝄋 ☐

staccato means:

accent ☐

fairly quick ☐

detached ☐

loud ☐

9 Look at this melody by C. Loewe and then answer the questions below.

Write your answer to question (b) on the stave below.

(a) (i)   The melody is in the key of A major. Name the degree
           of the scale (e.g. 2nd, 3rd) of the first note of the melody.   ....

    (ii)   Give the number of a bar that contains
           all the notes of the tonic triad of A major.   Bar ....

    (iii) Answer TRUE or FALSE to this sentence:

           Every bar in this melody contains at least one semiquaver (16th note).   ....

    (iv)   Give the letter name of the **lowest** note in the
           melody, including the sharp sign if necessary.   ....

    (v)   How many bars contain a dotted crotchet (dotted quarter-note)?   ....

(b) Copy out the music from the start of bar 1 to the end of bar 4, exactly as it is written
    above. Don't forget the clef, key signature, time signature, tempo marking, dynamics and
    all other details. Write the music on the blank stave above question (a).

| 10 |

| 10 |

Theory Paper   Grade 2   2017   C

Duration 1½ hours

TOTAL MARKS
100

Candidates should answer ALL questions.
Write your answers on this paper – no others will be accepted.
Answers must be written clearly and neatly – otherwise marks may be lost.

1 Add the time signature to each of these five examples.

10

2 Write the time values ♪. ♩ ♩. ♪ 𝅗𝅥 ♪ in the correct order, from the **shortest** to the **longest**. The first answer is given.

10

♪

....

3 **Above** each note write a **higher** note to form the named **harmonic** interval within the key of Bb major. The first answer is given. [10]

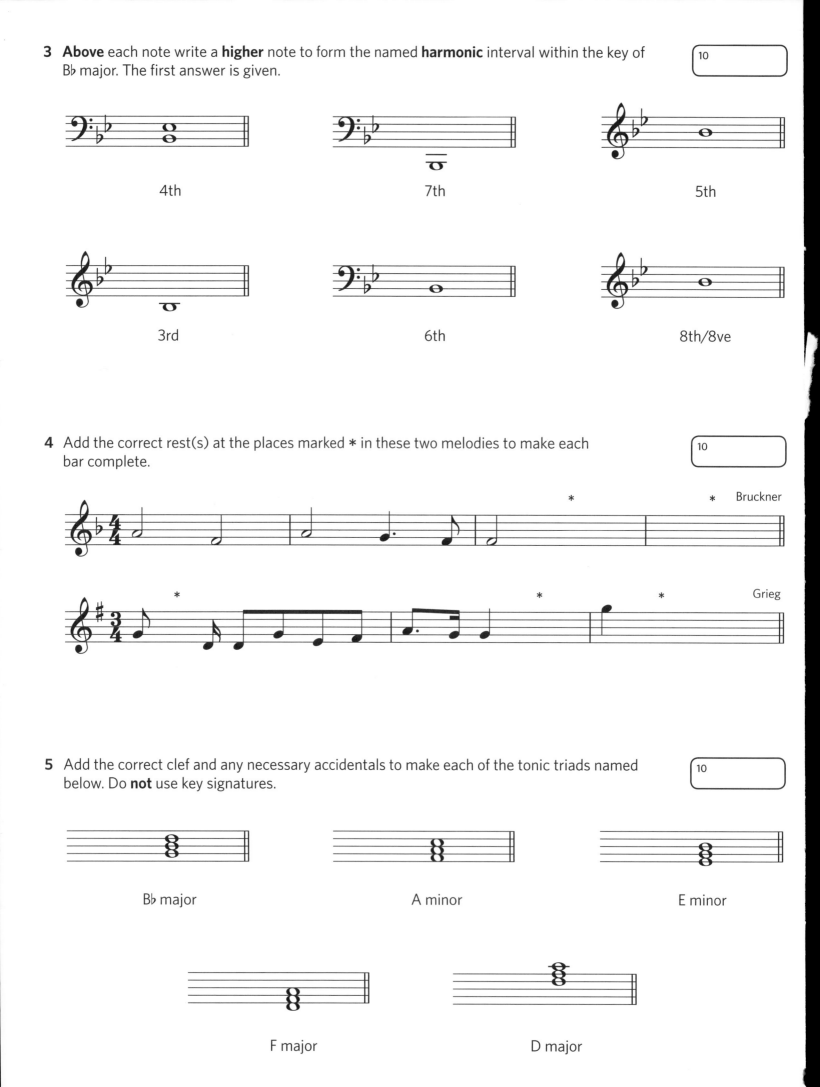

4th   7th   5th

3rd   6th   8th/8ve

4 Add the correct rest(s) at the places marked * in these two melodies to make each bar complete. [10]

Bruckner

Grieg

5 Add the correct clef and any necessary accidentals to make each of the tonic triads named below. Do **not** use key signatures. [10]

Bb major   A minor   E minor

F major   D major

6 Answer **both** (a) and (b).

10

(a) Give the letter name of each of the notes marked *, including the flat sign where necessary.
The first answer is given.

Franck

G
....

(b) How many semiquavers (16th notes) are the
tied notes in bar 1 (marked ↓) worth in total? ....

7 Rewrite the following melody in notes of **half the value**, beginning as shown.
Remember to group (beam) the notes correctly where necessary.

10

S. S. Wesley (adapted)

8 Tick one box for each term/sign, as shown in the first answer.

10

Presto means:		**Allegretto** means:		*giocoso* means:	
broadening	☐	gradually getting slower	☐	graceful	☐
at a medium speed	☐	fairly quick	☐	expressive	☐
rather slow	☐	gradually getting quicker	☐	playful, merry	☐
fast	✔	slow	☐	sweet	☐

fp means:		**rall.** means:		ˇ means:	
loud, then immediately quiet	☐	gradually getting quicker	☐	*staccato*	☐
forced, accented	☐	slow	☐	*staccatissimo*	☐
loud, gradually getting quieter	☐	gradually getting slower	☐	*sforzando*	☐
quiet, then immediately loud	☐	gradually getting louder	☐	*sostenuto*	☐

9 Look at this folksong melody and then answer the questions below.

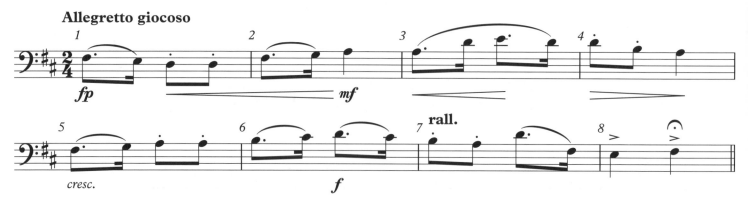

Write your answer to question (b) on the stave below.

(a) (i) The melody is in the key of D major. Name the degree
of the scale (e.g. 4th, 5th) of the first note of the melody. ....

☐ 10

(ii) Give the letter name of the **highest** note in the melody. ....

(iii) Answer TRUE or FALSE to this sentence:

The notes in bar 8 are to be played with accents. ....

(iv) In which bar is the performer told to pause or hold on to a note? Bar ....

(v) How many times does the rhythm ♩. ♪ occur? ....

(b) Copy out the music from the start of bar 5 to the end of bar 8, exactly as it is written
above. Don't forget the clef, key signature, dynamics and all other details. Write the
music on the blank stave above question (a).

☐ 10

Theory Paper   Grade 2   2017   S

Duration 1½ hours

TOTAL MARKS
100

Candidates should answer ALL questions.
Write your answers on this paper – no others will be accepted.
Answers must be written clearly and neatly – otherwise marks may be lost.

1   Add the time signature to each of these five examples.

10

2   Answer **both** (a) and (b).

10

(a) Name the degree of the scale (e.g. 2nd, 3rd) of each of the notes marked *, as shown in the
first answer. The key is E♭ major.

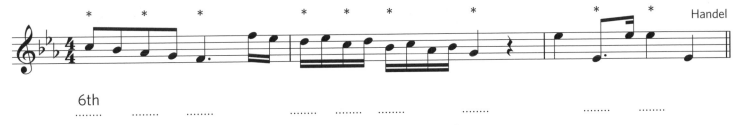

6th

(b) How many semiquavers (16th notes) is the last note of the melody worth?   ....

3 Write the tonic triads named below. Do **not** use key signatures but remember to put in any necessary accidentals.

10

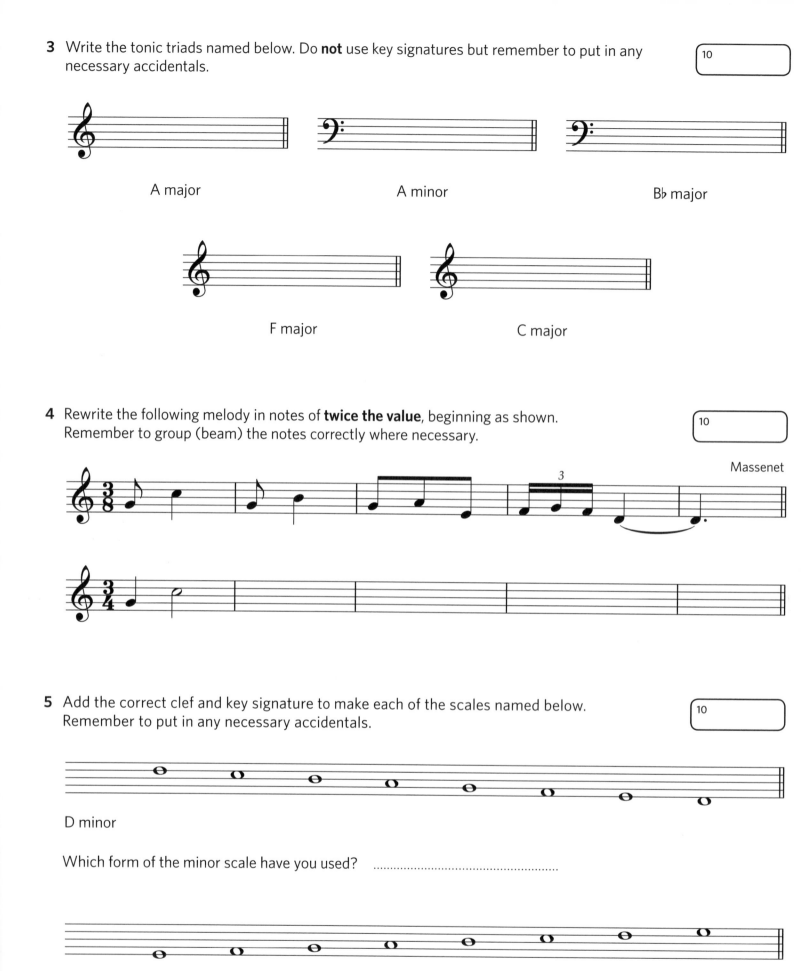

A major

A minor

B♭ major

F major

C major

4 Rewrite the following melody in notes of **twice the value**, beginning as shown. Remember to group (beam) the notes correctly where necessary.

10

Massenet

5 Add the correct clef and key signature to make each of the scales named below. Remember to put in any necessary accidentals.

10

D minor

Which form of the minor scale have you used? ....

G major

16

6 Add the correct rest(s) at the places marked * in these two melodies to make each bar complete. 10

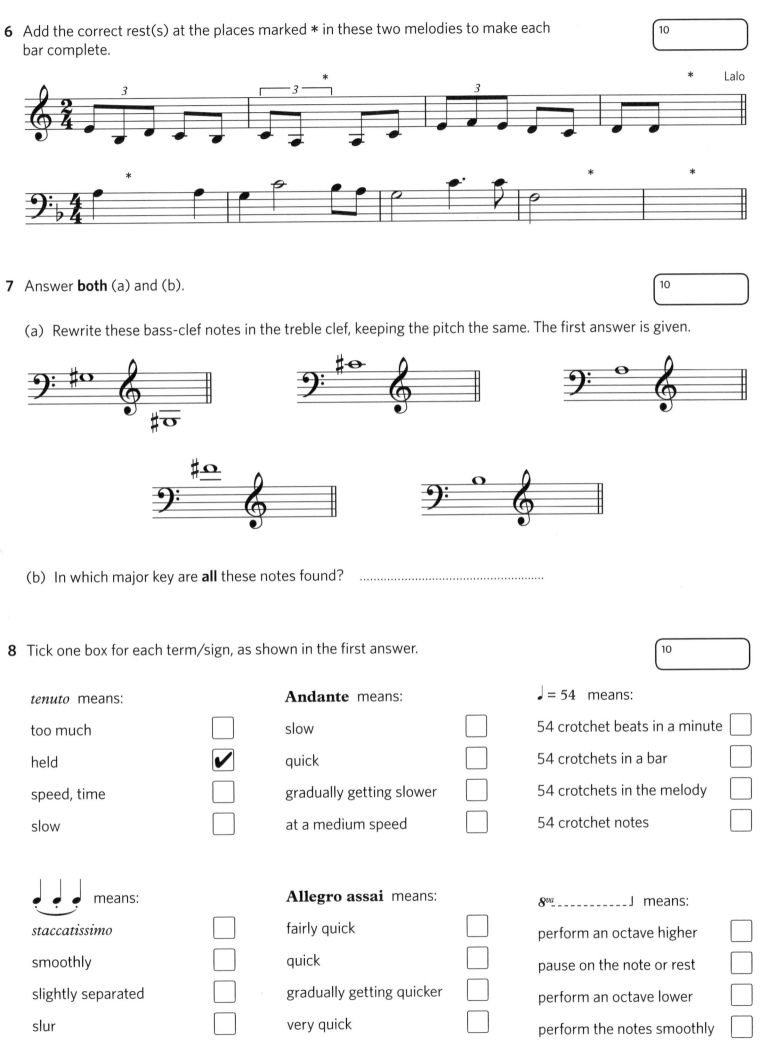

7 Answer **both** (a) and (b). 10

(a) Rewrite these bass-clef notes in the treble clef, keeping the pitch the same. The first answer is given.

(b) In which major key are **all** these notes found? ....

8 Tick one box for each term/sign, as shown in the first answer. 10

tenuto means:		**Andante** means:		♩ = 54 means:	
too much	☐	slow	☐	54 crotchet beats in a minute	☐
held	✔	quick	☐	54 crotchets in a bar	☐
speed, time	☐	gradually getting slower	☐	54 crotchets in the melody	☐
slow	☐	at a medium speed	☐	54 crotchet notes	☐

♩ ♩ ♩ means:		**Allegro assai** means:		8va_____⌐ means:	
staccatissimo	☐	fairly quick	☐	perform an octave higher	☐
smoothly	☐	quick	☐	pause on the note or rest	☐
slightly separated	☐	gradually getting quicker	☐	perform an octave lower	☐
slur	☐	very quick	☐	perform the notes smoothly	☐

9 Look at this melody, which is adapted from a piece by Grieg, and then answer the questions below.

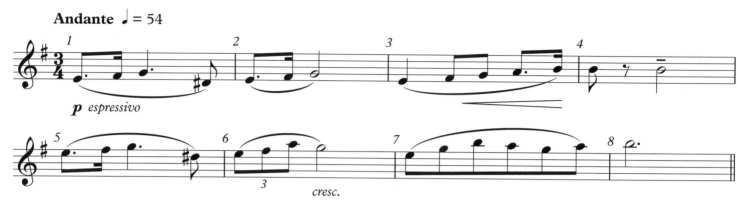

Write your answer to question (b) on the stave below.

(a) (i) How many semiquavers (16th notes)
is the last note of the melody worth? ....

(ii) Complete this sentence:

The triplet (♪♪♪) in bar 6 means
three quavers (eighth notes) in the time of ....

(iii) Answer TRUE or FALSE to this sentence:

All the notes in bars 1–4 of this melody can be found in the key of E minor. ....

(iv) Give the time name (e.g. crotchet or
quarter note) of the **rest** in bar 4. ....

(v) Underline one of the following words that describes how bar 3
should be played.

legato (smoothly)   or   *staccato* (detached)

(b) Copy out the music from the start of bar 5 to the end of bar 8, exactly as it is written   [10]
above. Don't forget the clef, key signature, dynamic and all other details. Write the music
on the blank stave above question (a).